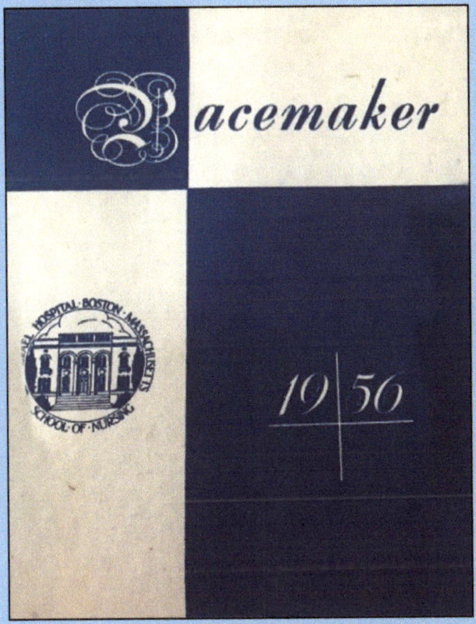

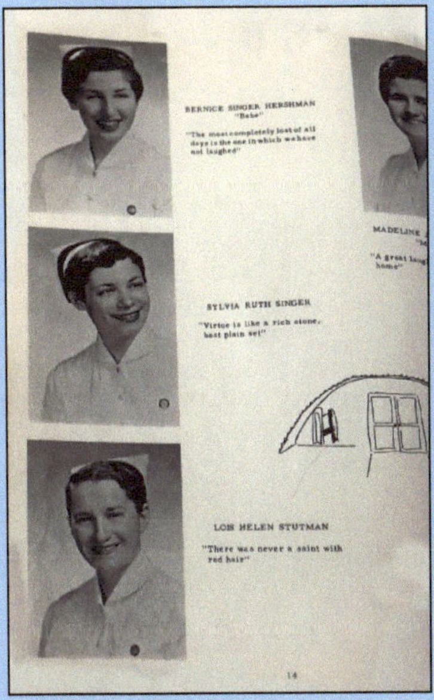

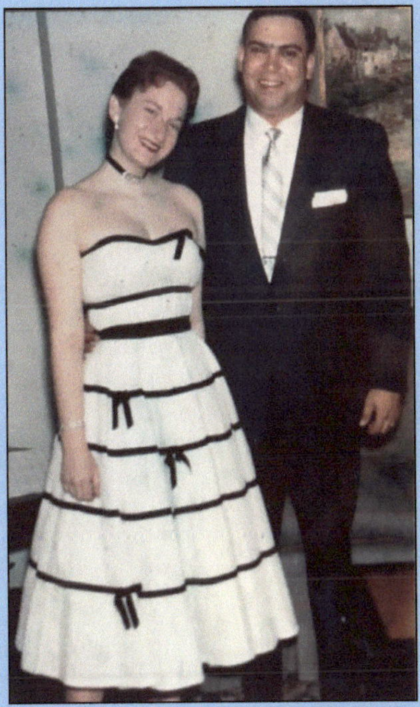

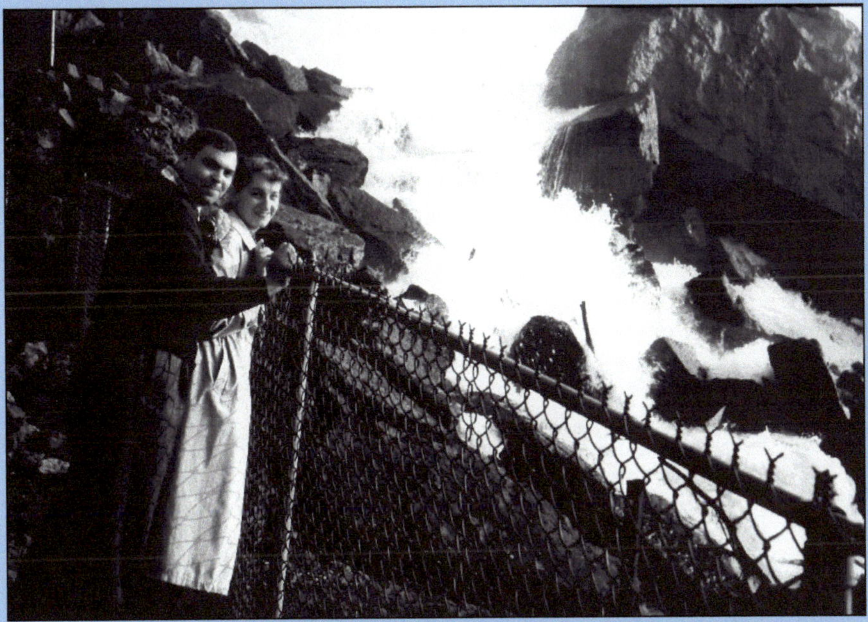

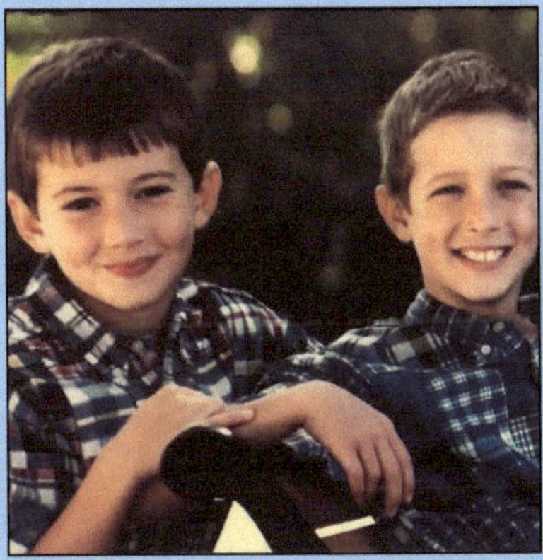

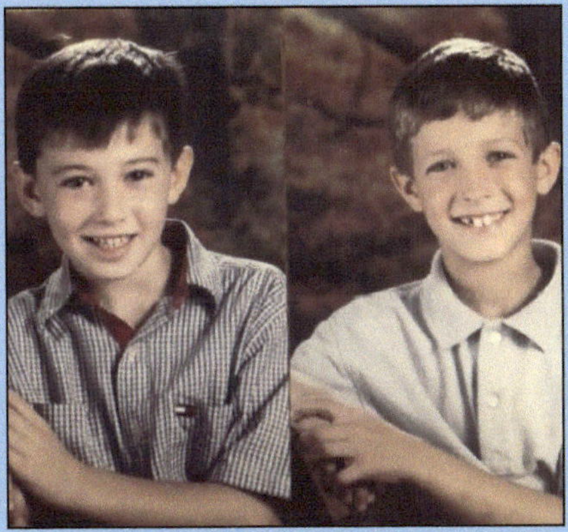

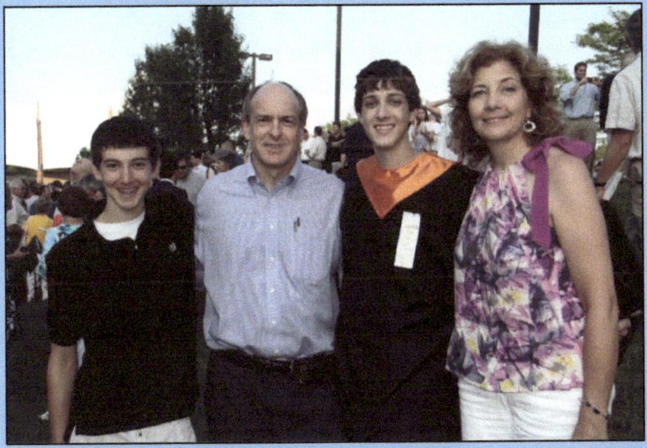

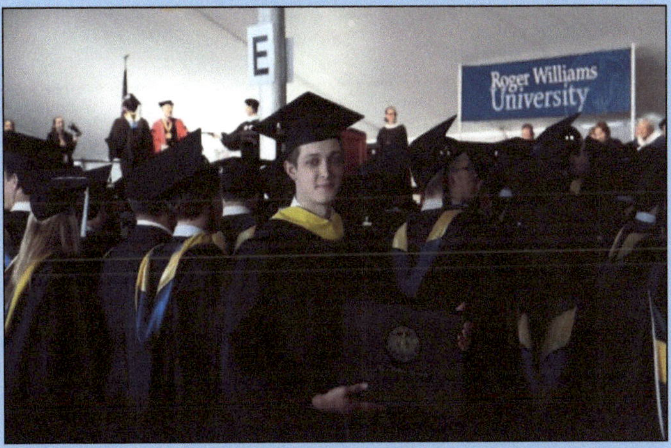

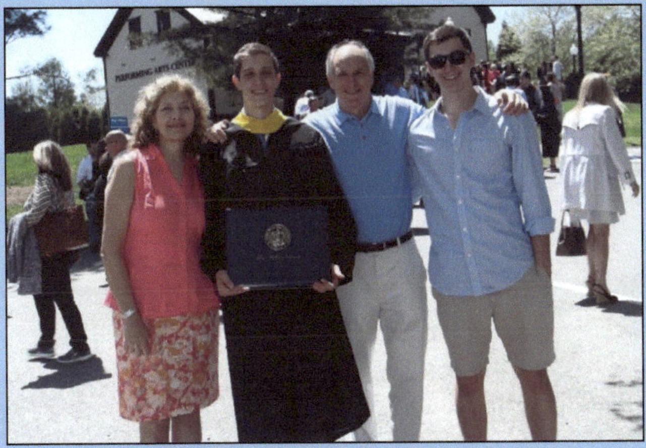

www.ingramcontent.com/pod-product-compliance
Lightning Source LLC
Chambersburg PA
CBHW040918200926
51546CB00007B/55
9781952521461

MY LEGACY STORY

LOIS HELEN STUTMAN ROSENFIELD

My Legacy Story

Produced and printed
by Stillwater River Publications.

Visit our website at
www.StillwaterPress.com
for more information.

First Stillwater River Publications Edition

ISBN: 978-1-952521-461

1 2 3 4 5 6 7 8 9 10
Written by Lois Rosenfield
Published by Stillwater River Publications,
Pawtucket, RI, USA.

Dedication

To my amazing children Michael and Elaine with love...

Acknowledgements

To Elaine who said, "Mom, you have to do this Legacy book," and I did.

To David, my husband, who was by my side for 62 years and left me this story to complete.
I miss you…

To Debbie Rich – my typist who did all my stories with pleasure and friendship – so grateful.

To all others who helped in their own way to be a part of this person's legacy.

Maurice And Ida's wedding, June 28, 1921

Introduction

Here is my story – written at a different time in this world –
one which we were unprepared for but met with a challenge and will hopefully win over.

As said by all – Be safe and Be well!

Lois and David's wedding, October 21, 1956.

A Legacy
to
Remember

My life began on a cool night on October 22, 1935.
My sister being 13 years old, must have known our mama was pregnant but not about the birthing process happening upstairs in the bedroom. She sat crying and hugging the dog on the porch as our mother was screaming in pain. I was born, and a breech baby also, and we both survived. As I am writing this I have just turned 84 years old and my sister is a young 97.

Our brother Bob was sleeping and with the wails of our mother, and the new baby crying, he marched into the bedroom rubbing his 6-year-old eyes and stated, "throw that cat down the cellar. I can't sleep!"

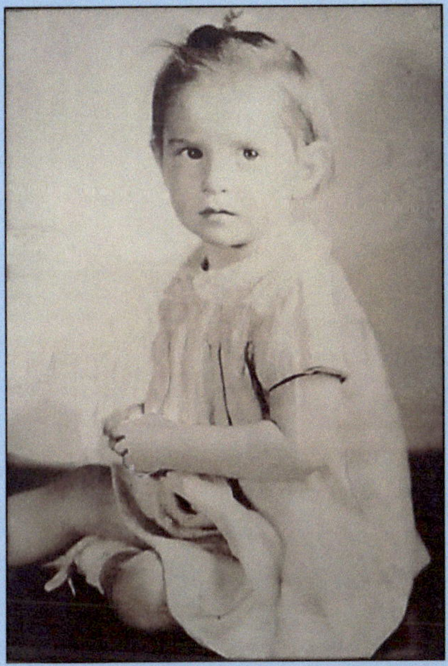

Lois at 1.

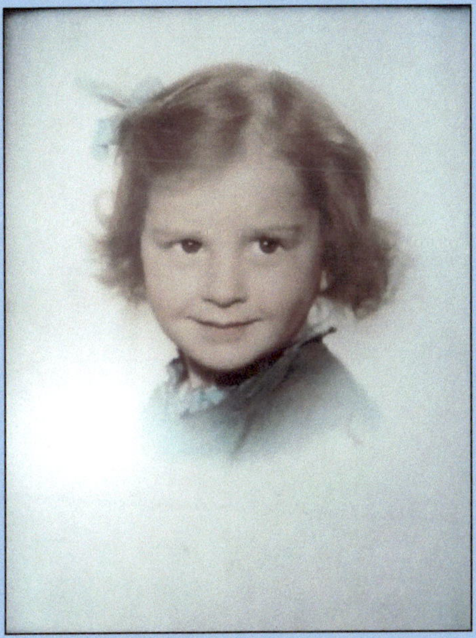

Lois at 5.

Lois and Daddy, 1936.

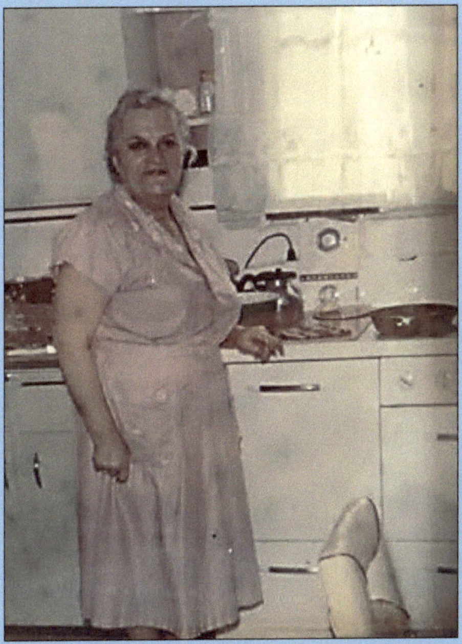

My mom.

The home I was born in, Franklin, Massachusetts.

Life began at 37 Highland Street in Franklin, Massachusetts where I lived until I graduated high school in 1953. That famous class of students are forever friends even after our 65th class reunion in 2018. Seventeen years went by with all my ups and downs that occurred!

A favorite memory is the Hurricane of '38 - I was not yet 3 years old and remember watching the storm from our front door and my own 16-year-old sister holding my hand. She held my hand for so many years to come, and now I am the hand holder and doer for her as she resides in respite living.

I remember my tiny but warm bedroom, my bed and dresser, my bedside table and lamp, and radio. No TV or cells then and no house alarms, with just a thin skeleton key to lock the front door.

I was happy to have my family with me, even when I was not yet 10 years old and Auntie Becky lived with us. I had to sleep on a couch pullout bed in my parents' bedroom until she moved to Brighton, Massachusetts, and then to Boston where she was a treasurer of a bank on Mass Avenue - an achievement for this woman in the later years of the 1940s. She was the first valedictorian in high school until I became valedictorian in junior high in 1949, the year my future husband David was a junior in college in Rhode Island!

In addition to our immediate family there was my father's brother, Hyman Stutman, his wife Nellie, and their two children Leonard and Eleanor. Leonard was to become a cardiologist and Eleanor a mother of three boys and a mediation counselor in Tiburon, California. She passed away just recently on January 16, 2020.

On my mother's side of the family were my grandparents, Joseph and Etta Katseff and their seven children with my mother Ida being the oldest, followed by Belle, Sarah, Anne, Golyde, Samuel (Uncle Mulky), and Albert (Uncle Honey). They all producing my many cousins, Rhoda Freedman,

Harvey Freedman, Shirley Freedman, Richard Holmes, Susan Russian, Jerry Russin, Howard Katseff, Peter Katseff, and Linda, Robbie, Ellen and Jimmy Katseff.

My cousins, did not have the times at our grandparents' farm that I did as a young girl - even my sister and brother did not as much. It seems I was there so much sharing time with my still unmarried Aunt Belle who basically was in charge of the farm in the early forties along with my Uncle Honey and my grandparents.

Lois and Jerry on a horse, 1942.

I slept in the same bedroom as Aunt Belle and worked along with her helping with the farm chores - feeding the foxes she raised which made many fur coats in the 1940s, helping to outfox them when they got out of their inner pen, and of course picking up the eggs the chickens laid. I made ground horsemeat into giant meatballs for the foxes and helping to deliver the 'wrapped bundles' of horsemeat for the dog kennels. I rode horses with my uncle, and at the farm in Ashland when I was alone I would walk into the barn and kick every cow that was laying down in the rear to make them stand up - up and down the length of the barn on both sides - the best achievement that a 10-year-old could have!

Other memories are going to the banks to deposit all the money with Aunt Belle, and the wonderful ice cream I was treated to afterwards, and our swims in Lake Winthrop in the summertime, plus all the family holidays celebrated on the farm, and sneaking up to the attic to peer into the trunks of stuff with my cousins and having no fear at all - a great opportunity I had.

I graduated high school in June of 1953 and went to Beth Israel School of Nursing in Boston, Massachusetts. My mother remained in the house in Franklin until she sold it and moved to Woonsocket, Rhode Island to live with Edythe and her family in later 1955.

My nursing career from 1953 - 1956 was at Beth Israel Hospital in Boston, Massachusetts and then after graduation and finishing in September of 1956 – then my wedding to David Rosenfield.

Lois in second grade , Brick schoolhouse.

Lois' high school yearbook

RUSSELL STEWART
34 Winter St. Franklin, Mass.
"Russ"
Virtue: Teeth
Vice: Shyness
Suppressed Desire: To join the U. S. Air Force
Usually found: In Dana's
Russ is one of the shy boys in our class, but when you get to know him you'll find out he's a swell kid. We know you'll achieve your desire because "nothing can stop the U. S. Air Force."
Activities: Chess Club 1

To "Lois" Good luck and the best of wishes in the future "Russ"

LOIS HELEN STUTMAN
37 Highland St. Franklin, Mass.
"Stuty"
Virtue: Wit
Vice: Exaggeration
Suppressed Desire: To become an R.N.
Usually found: With Roberta
"Stuty" is one of our good humor girls who can usually be found with her good pal, Roberta. She is quite the intellect too and we know with her intelligence she has what it takes to be a success.
Activities: Hockey, Basketball, Volleyball, Badminton, Softball 1-4; Glee Club 1; Sports Club 3, 4; Prom Committee 3; Yearbook Staff 4; Oskey 1-4; Grand March 3, 4; Dance Committees 2, 3, 4; Blue and White 2; Bulletin 2; Driver Ed. 3.

Lois' high school yearbook picture

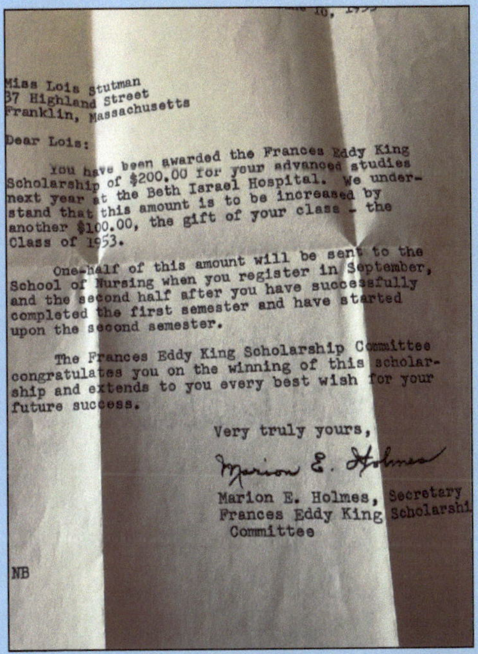

Miss Lois Stutman
37 Highland Street
Franklin, Massachusetts

Dear Lois:

You have been awarded the Frances Eddy King Scholarship of $200.00 for your advanced studies next year at the Beth Israel Hospital. We understand that this amount is to be increased by another $100.00, the gift of your class - the Class of 1953.

One-half of this amount will be sent to the School of Nursing when you register in September, and the second half after you have successfully completed the first semester and have started upon the second semester.

The Frances Eddy King Scholarship Committee congratulates you on the winning of this scholarship and extends to you every best wish for your future success.

Very truly yours,

Marion E. Holmes

Marion E. Holmes, Secretary
Frances Eddy King Scholarshi
Committee

NB

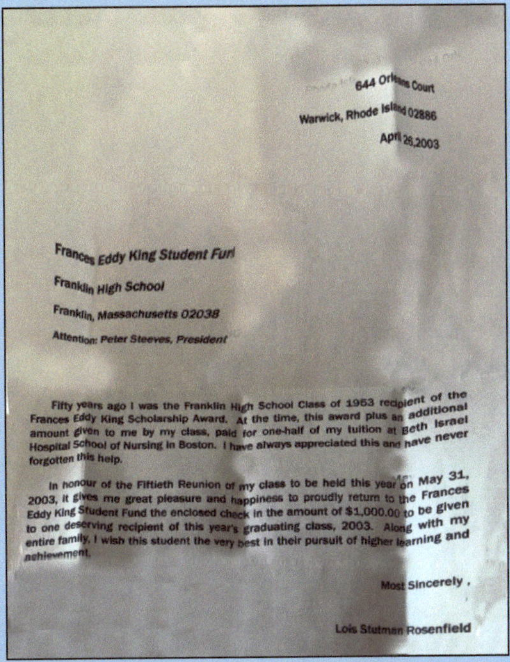

644 Orleans Court
Warwick, Rhode Island 02886
April 26,2003

Frances Eddy King Student Fund
Franklin High School
Franklin, Massachusetts 02038
Attention: Peter Steeves, President

Fifty years ago I was the Franklin High School Class of 1953 recipient of the Frances Eddy King Scholarship Award. At the time, this award plus an additional amount given to me by my class, paid for one-half of my tuition at Beth Israel Hospital School of Nursing in Boston. I have always appreciated this and have never forgotten this help.

In honour of the Fiftieth Reunion of my class to be held this year on May 31, 2003, it gives me great pleasure and happiness to proudly return to the Frances Eddy King Student Fund the enclosed check in the amount of $1,000.00 to be given to one deserving recipient of this year's graduating class, 2003. Along with my entire family, I wish this student the very best in their pursuit of higher learning and achievement.

Most Sincerely ,

Lois Stutman Rosenfield

Left: *Lois' scholarship award letter, June 1953.*
Right: *Lois' donation to the scholarship in 2003, at the time of her 50th class reunion..*

Lois' high school graduating class, 1953.

Photos from Lois' 30th, 50th and 65th high school reunions.

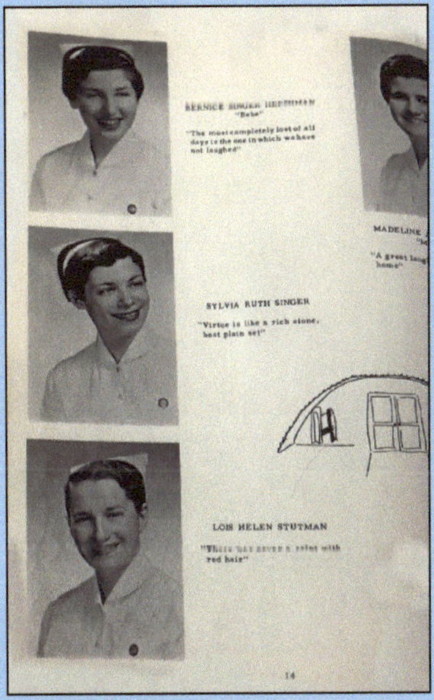

Lois' nursing yearbook and photo from Beth Israel Hospital, 1956.

Lois and David's prom picture.

Lois and David on their honeymoon.

David and I re-met (as my Aunt Anne and his Uncle Ben were married in 1934) on a train home from Boston, Massachusetts in September of 1955, when I was not yet 20 years old. He drove me to my home from the train and the rest is history as we soon started to date, and were two quickies to be together. By Thanksgiving 1955 I had a beautiful emerald-cut one carat flawless diamond ring and we were engaged and set a wedding date for October 21, 1956.

My mother arranged a wonderful wedding for David and I and our families were happy to hear very soon after that we were expecting a baby, Michael, born on July 20, 1957 in Boston at Beth Israel Hospital. We first lived in Brookline, Massachusetts and then moved to Albany, New York.

My return to nursing wasn't until almost six years after my mother died in 1958 - a tragic error during surgery of colon resections at MGH in Boston where the surgeon lost a sponge in the closing count and she had to go back into surgery soon after to retrieve the sponge. Five days later, in my care, she died quickly of a blood clot when my son was just one-year old - this gave me much sadness and depression for a long time, blaming myself for the error - not the doctor.

I became pregnant then and the pregnancy was not a good one and I miscarried at four and a half months and was told I had to wait before another pregnancy due to an 0 negative blood problem.

We had to go on and my life was difficult with a young one-year-old child and I was sad about what had happened. My mother gone, we decided to move to our first home in Colonie, New York outside Albany - an adorable first home, and there Elaine was born to us. She arrived just 25 minutes after I got to the Albany Medical Center Hospital on April 13, 1961 in a snowstorm. My lipstick was on her forehead when David saw her so quickly after I gave birth to her. It was not like when Michael was born and David left me off at Beth Israel Hospital in Boston as he had to go home to eat, shower, read the paper, and watch the news on TV until he got the call from the hospital that his son was born. Michael was born at 10:48 PM on July 20, 1957 just 10 minutes until the 11 PM news. We had two children now and a beagle puppy called Tookie.

We had many memories of our ranch house in New York living there for two years. Michael had two best friends, brothers Keith and Dennis, and Elaine, a baby did celebrate her first birthday there and many relatives visited.

David was transferred to Rhode Island for his job with the Federal Highway Administration - formerly the Bureau of Public Roads. Our new home was on 137 Baldwin Road in Warwick, Rhode Island and it was our address for the next 26 years.

So much happened in Warwick, Rhode Island for me and the entire family - our home was in a new plat of homes: Colonials, ranches, split-levels and one Cape Cod. There were many children and many friends for the children to grow up with and to go to elementary school, junior high, and eventually graduate high school with many memories that became their world.

I started back to nursing doing a bit of private duty then and as the children grew older I did staff at Kent County Hospital - then as the years passed staff did private duty in most of the major hospitals in Rhode Island.

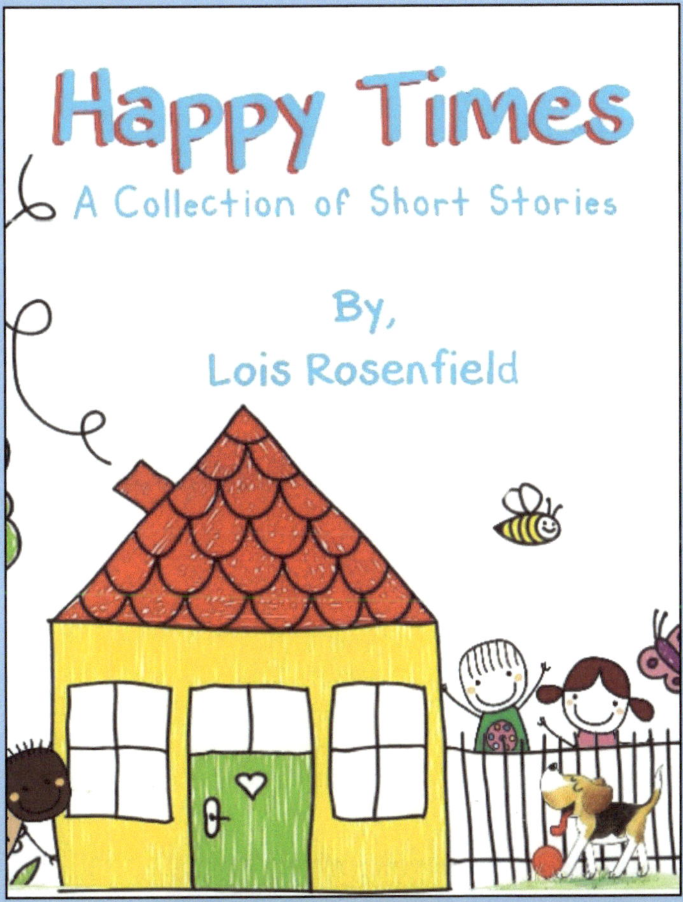

Happy Times book signing, December 2018.

Left side, front to back: *Lois, Zayde, and Bob.*
Right side, front to back: *Eleanor, My dad's brother Hyman, and Lenny.*

Left to right*: David, Ellie, Lois, and Harry*

Family Reunion

KATSEFF FAMILY

"Bella's Wedding 1946"

DATE: August 14, 2010 (4PM – 11PM)

WHERE: Hilton Garden Inn
1 Thurber Street
Warwick, Rhode Island
Tel: (401)734-9600

TIME: Cocktails & Hors D'oeuvres
(Cash Bar)
Buffet Dinner, Dessert, Music & Dancing

All with your long-lost cousins!

$50 - adults, $25 - Children 12 & under

Please RSVP by June 15 to Lois Rosenfield

644 Orleans Ct Warwick, RI 02886., (Tel: 401-737-6149) Darsnfld@aol.com

AdultTotal:___ Name #1__________ Name #2__________ Name #3__________ Name #4__________

ChildrenTotal:___ Name #1__________ Name #2__________ Name #3__________ Name #4__________

Total $ enclosed:________ **(checks made payable to Lois Rosenfield)** **(OVER)**

Katseff family reunion invitation, August 14, 2010

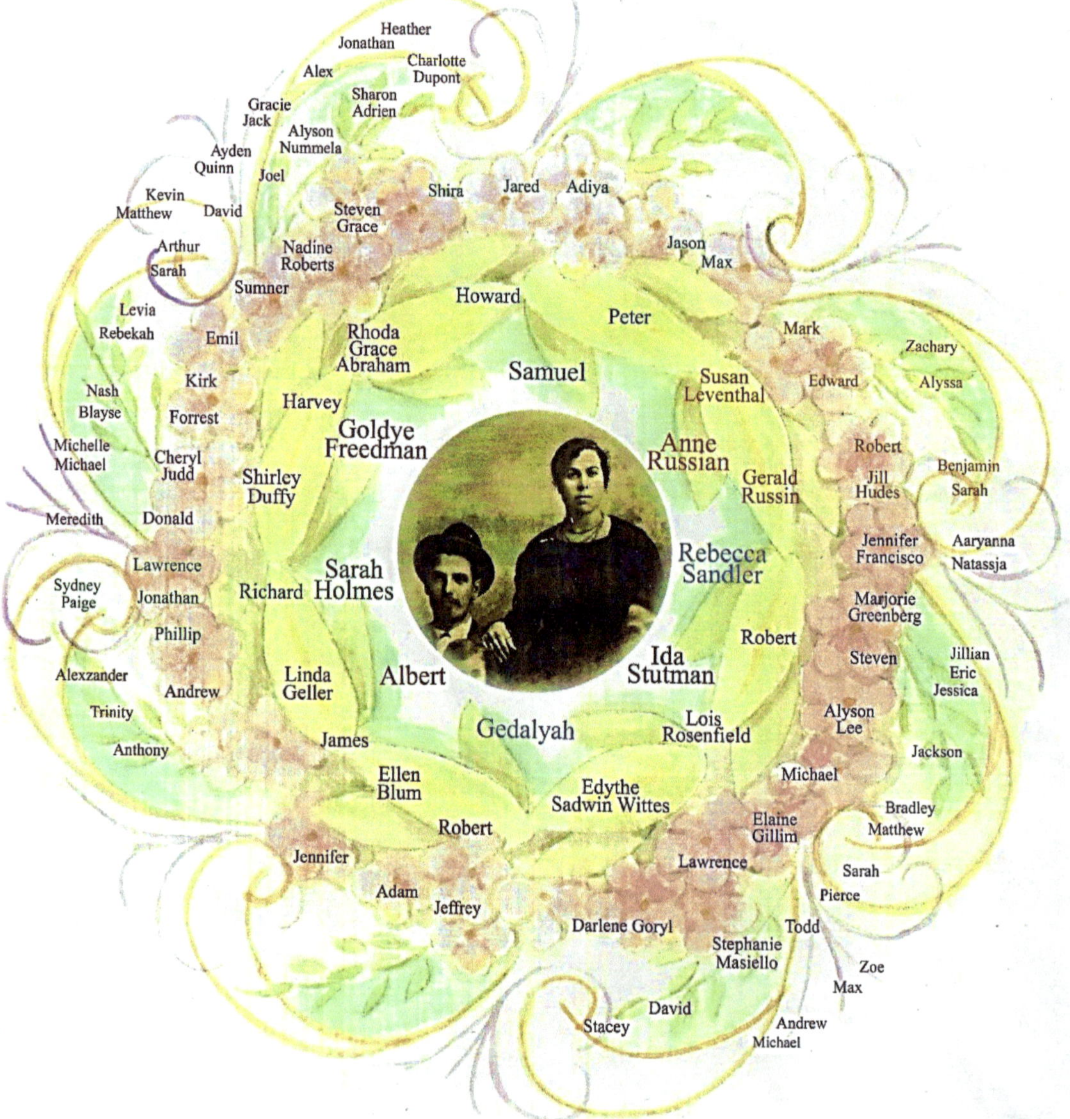

August 14, 2010 - Warwick, Rhode Island
Reunion of the Descendants of
Joseph and Etta Leah (Chait) Katseff
married December 11, 1897 in Birzai, Lithuania

The Katseff grandparents, Joseph and Etta Leah (Chait) Katseff.

Our family picture

Left: *Edie and Lois.* **Right:** *Edie, Lois, and Bob.*

Our 50th wedding anniversary

David, Lois and Mike.

Pete, Judy, Lois, and David

The Mah Jongg gals: Hilda, Judy, Lois, Jen, and Melanie.

Judy and Pete.

Darlene and Lois: South County Hospital Luncheon, June 2019

New York wedding, October 2018: Peter, Lois, and Howard.

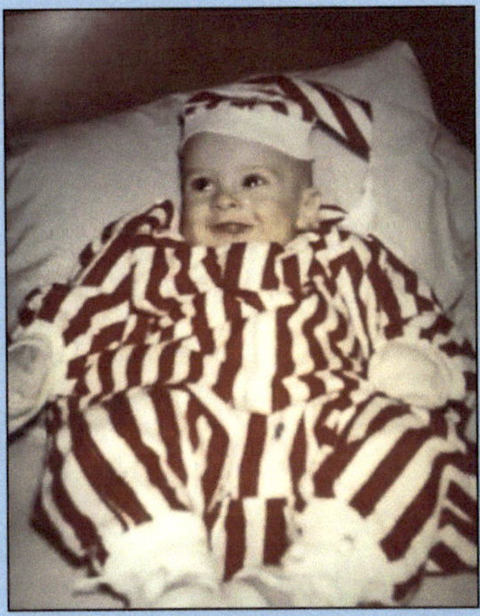

Mike as a baby.

Mike and Elaine.

Elaine and Mike, early 1962.

Clockwise from top*:*
Elaine and Mike with Frisky Jane; Elaine and Mike; David at home on Baldwin Road; and Elaine, David, and Bitsy

Clockwise from top: *David, Elaine, and Lois; Two of the family: Lois, David, Elaine, and Mike, and Mother's Day at 137 Baldwin Road, Warwick..*

Our life there was the growing-up time for Mike and 'Lainsy' as she was called then. There were many friends and fun times - many birthdays to celebrate and parties to give. Hot times. I still had periods of depression from the loss of my mother but I became better and so much was able to be done and we had the best Bar Mitzvah celebrations for Michael when the grass on the front lawn looked like velvet and Elaine's many birthday parties, proms and the graduation party from UVM with me part of the time checking on her girlfriend upstairs on her bed with a very bad sunburn. The college days for both our children took place at UVM one after the other.

Michael going on to Berkeley for his Master's and PhD in Engineering and Elaine making Phi Beta Kappa and going on to be a finance expert and making lots of money for herself before even marriage.

Mike started with IBM during the summer from Berkeley and becoming an actual member of their staff after graduating in 1983. Elaine graduated from UVM in 1983 - a banner year for us all - we went on.

Soon it was time to meet the girl that Michael brought home and they soon became an engaged couple and then a wedding planned for him and Beth Mitenbuler. At this time David and I decided to move out of our Baldwin Road home and we did so in July of 1988.

David was having back problems and the outside lawn work became too much for him and as all marriages go, we had problems and we decided we would move to a condo; and things changed for the good for us. It was 100 degrees that day and the full air conditioning in the condo cooled us. I was the "Charles in Charge" of our move as David's back was a problem. I look back and wonder how I did it all! The condo was much smaller than the house but we made do and then lots started to happen for the next of years.

Michael and Beth were married on May 7, 1989 in Portsmouth, Rhode Island on a beautiful spring day and their rehearsal dinner was at the Ivy Lodge in Newport the night before - on both days I wore beautiful dresses and was a proud mom. David was a proud dad also.

We had an after party in the condo and many people came as did the newly married couple in their limo that eventually took them to Boston and then they went on their honeymoon to Kauai in Hawaii and New Zealand and then back to Connecticut.

I remember a lot of good times but sometimes in my life I revert to the times not good and then it takes time to get back on the good track. I survive and I've tried to be a survivor as I have always had my job to do and that is important in life.

We became first grandparents in May of 1992 when our Matthew was born just a day after my sister Edie's 70th birthday. We, David and I, rushed to see our new grandson the next day and held this new little one in our arms.

As grandparents we did see the necessity to help and had this shared great joy. He, Matthew, was just about 1 and a half years old when Elaine married Jonathan Gillim on September 11, 1993 - a lovely wedding on the beach at Cliffside on Nantucket. Many came to this wedding and soon after our second reception at Wethersfield in October 1993. We learned that Michael and Beth were expecting baby #2, born on May 15, 1994 and Matthew suddenly had a little brother Bradley and our duties increased as we helped out as much as we could and shared the joy of their early years with fun, games, and sports.

A young Elaine.

Elaine's high school picture.

Elaine's college photograph.

Elaine's high school graduation.

Mike's Berkeley PhD graduation, May 1984.

Mike's Berkeley PhD graduation, May 1984.

Mike's first ride on the IBM private jet.

Brad and Matt.

Matt's high school graduation:
Brad, Mike, Matt, and Beth.

Matt's college graduation.

Matt's college graduation:
Beth, Matt, Mike, and Brad.

Brad's high school graduation; Beth, Brad, Mike, and Matt.

Brad's college graduation.

Brad's college graduation; Mike, Brad, Beth, and Matt.

Ailish, Matt, Sarah, Brad, and Pierce.

Elaine became pregnant just at the time David retired from the Department of Transportation in September of 1997.

Our beautiful and only grand-daughter Sarah was born on April 19, 1998 and a joy to behold - a little girl and my daughter had her own daughter - a joy. Again our job and joy was to help out and both of us did just that and shared the love of their dog - a Wheaten Terrier called 'Gloria.' Life was happier and very busy.

Soon, two years later, Elaine had her second child Pierce in the new millennium in 2000 on January 25. A talent to be who was to become a singer and dancer and a wonderful young man.

I sometimes think how life carries itself in stages one after the other and you climb those steps together.

I sometimes wish my mother could have lived to see her other grandchildren being born and great-grandchildren, as well as my dad who died too early from a stroke during my senior year of high school in September of 1952. Their love would have been a joy to see but was missed by me with their early passing - even at this later age of my life I still think of them and miss them.

I would like to talk a bit about my two parents at length as they were two very interesting people having grown up in houses with just a big field separating them where they began their love across the field.

Maurice had two siblings both born in the US - he being born in 1893 in an area of Russia called Bresalee Volinsky Guberny and came to the United States with his parents, Louis and Elizabeth at about 4 years of age and made their home in West Medway, Mass. There, Hyman and Rebecca were born and Louis was a farmer by trade.

Maurice was a baseball player at Medway High School and had been trained at Wentworth as an electrician. When WWI started he was drafted into the Army he was sent to France and was one of the first people to set up the communications lines and was gassed but not hurt.

He came home and married his love, Ida, my mother and they lived in Medway where Edythe was born on May 23, 1922 and who was cared for by her young uncles Mulky and Honey.

Maurice and Ida moved to Franklin, Massachusetts where my brother Robert Elwood was born on November 9, 1929 maybe bringing on the crash of '29 as he was a devil from birth on. I came into the world six years later in 1935.

Maurice had a hard life as he had many repercussions from the war and at times used alcohol to help him along but it gave great fearful times to his wife and children. He lived to see Edythe and Robert marry and to see two of his grand-children born to Edythe and her husband Sherwood - Larry and Darlene. Three strokes and he died on September 14, 1952 when I had just entered my senior year in high school.

Ida grew up near my father on her parents' farm in West Medway and there were five sisters and then two brothers to be born. I know she helped my Bubbe Etta in the house and farm chores also. She married Maurice on June 28, 1921.

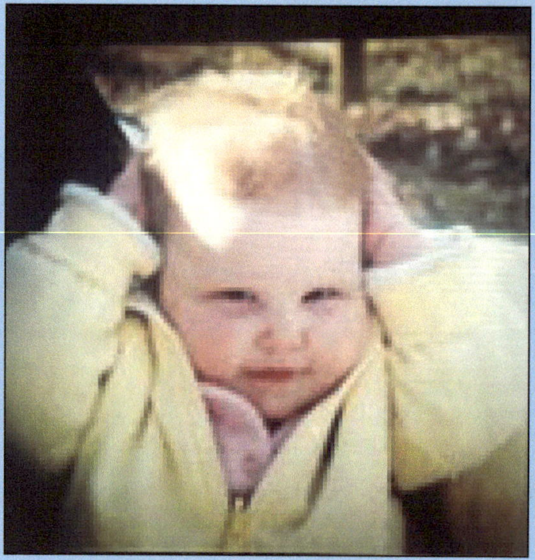

Sarah as a baby.

Lois' 70th birthday party. From left to right: Beth, Lois, Sarah, and Elaine, October 2005.

Sarah

Sarah, high school graduation with Poppa.

Sarah and Elaine.

Elaine, Sarah, and Pierce.

Sarah's URI graduation, May 2020.

Pierce at a concert with Gram and Poppa

Pierce's high school graduation with Lois and David.

Sarah, Pierce, Lois and Elaine, Wellsfleet 2019.

Pierce in his prom jacket

New York wedding 1997.

Class reunion.

Lois and David at FHA Retirement 1986.

Sunny View 2019

My mother was a wonderful, kind and gentle lady who did her work which was not easy in those times without the help of today - for so many years. She cooked on a wood stove and had yes an ice box until much later a refrigerator and regular electric stove. The favorite spot in her kitchen was the basket filled with old clothes to sit on in front of the hot water heater. We three siblings fought for that one spot in the winter. She worked for the Red Cross in the 1940s during WWII to roll bandages and do whatever else was needed and in my early high school years opened a combined dress shop and housewares store in the town. I worked there during my high school years until she had to close the store. I even measured women for corsets that she sold. I always wondered if they fit the women?

She endured my father's drinking as we all did but still loved him until his death. After he died we (she and I) had a difficult time and we went to my grandparent's a lot to stay.

David's family was his mom and dad, Bessie and Hyman and he had one brother Zolman and his sister Gloria and their families - six nieces and nephews with Barbara, David, Annie and Jenny being Zol and Lil's children and Steven and Peter being Gloria and Jack's children. There were many aunts and uncles in David's family with Lena, Jacob, Annie, Maurice, Benjamin and Marshie and Freda as Bessie's siblings and Marcus and Minnie as Hyman's only brother and sister in law with their two children. It was a big family.

David lost his dad in 1959, his mother in 1976 and his brother and sister in 1983 and 1984 - both in their mid-sixties. David passed on January 18, 2019 at 91 years of age.

I remember our good years together and the many parties and fun we had until David's health started to decline in 1992 with surgeries and a stroke in September of 2003 and the entire time of caregiving of more than 26 years that was hard and difficult for me but I did it all.

How do you describe a lifetime lived with all the events that occurred - so much to describe as that is a life lived and suddenly in the most glorious distance suddenly it is 2020 - a new decade and as now I be soon to celebrate my 85th birthday I reflect on my time lived until now.

2000 was the new millennium year and we celebrated here - David and I, Edythe, and Robert and Eveline. We toasted in this new year with joy and Chinese food - together! Bob was to pass away just seventeen years later from kidney problems and Edie was in assisted living after a stroke in January of 2017 with speech problems and still the vibrant person she was.

I believe that joy comes first in this year 2000 as on January 25 our youngest grandson was born- Pierce - and the new millennium begins its job and carries on.

Sitting and reflecting on times I look back to all I did and have to pat myself on the back a few times. I did my nursing for so many years, staff and private duty and can write a book alone about the career and what about my next career, Real Estate and moi became a Realtor. I sold lots of houses and enjoyed the fun of it, what a joy to take an offer on a house and follow it through to closing. I met a lot of people and new friends along the way.

I was volunteering at the same time at Hasbro Children's Hospital emergency room and prior to that in Rhode Island Hospital. At the ER I did so many chores and even taught the volunteers there. At the time my Prudential Real Estate was having a community service contest and awards for Realtors across the entire country and my boss-lady said I should enter the contest. I did not want to but she said I should and I did. Guess I should have as I won the Top 5 in the entire country and the

COMMUNITY *Champs*

The Prudential Foundation recently awarded more than /5 grants, ranging from $215 to $5,000 to Prudential Real Estate Network members on behalf of its Community Champions Program. The annual program recognizes affiliates who exemplify outstanding public service in their communities. The Prudential Real Estate Affiliates, Inc. would like to recognize all grant recipients for their volunteer work and dedication to the non-profit organizations and service groups in which they are involved by listing their names below.

The five individuals pictured are recipients of the Community Champions Golden Star Award.

Lois Rosenfield
Prudential Prime Properties

Don Cohen
Prudential America West Real Estate

Steve Janett
Prudential Janett Real Estate

David Flory
Prudential Carolinas Realty

Walt Schopfer
Prudential Floberg REALTORS®

Greg Armstrong	Prudential Tropical Realty, New Port Richey, FL
Jacqueline Anne Austin	Prudential Dwyer Schlecte REALTORS® Inc., Jackson, MI
Karen Belden	Prudential DeHOFF REALTORS®, North Canton, OH
Wende Bell	Prudential Southwest Realty, Las Vegas, NV
Richard Bennett	Prudential Snook, REALTORS®, Cameron, MO
John Beranek	Prudential Triple S Realty, Durango, CO
Robert Billimack	Prudential Town Square Realty, Woodstock, IL
Martin Bittick	Prudential Bittick Realty, Jackson, MS
Gladys Blum	Prudential Real Estate Professionals, Salem, OR
Kathie Brewer	Prudential Botts & Associates REALTORS®, Cleveland, TN
Robert Brooks	Prudential Habs Real Estate, Bedford, NH
Charlotte Burger	Prudential Residenz REALTORS®, Beavercreek, OH
Paul Butler	Prudential California Realty, Del Mar, CA
G. Christman	Prudential Floberg REALTORS®, Billings, MT
Michael Cocciolo	Prudential Pacific Properties, Florence, OR
Don Cohen	Prudential American West Real Estate, Bakersfield, CA
Craig Colburn	Prudential Dunn REALTORS®, San Diego, CA
Jim Colvin	Prudential Lindrick Realty, Inc., New Port Richey, FL
Mary Cook	Prudential Volunteer Realty, Knoxville, TN
Bob Cottrell	Prudential O'Brien & Associates, Inc., Dillon, CO
Nancy Duran	Prudential Stewart Realty, Closter, NJ
Cathy Echterling	Prudential Summers REALTORS®, St. Joseph, MO
Robert Felte	Prudential Felte Real Estate, Willow Grove, PA
David Flory	Prudential Carolinas Realty, Wrightsville Beach, NC
Suzie Gasper	Prudential California Realty, Fremont, CA
Patricia Gerber	Prudential DeHoFF REALTORS®, North Canton, OH
Marvin Ginn	Prudential Preferred Properties, Albuquerque, NM
Tracey Goetz	Prudential Carolinas Realty, Durham, NC
Marilyn Haas	Prudential C. Dan Joyner Co., REALTORS®, Greer, SC
Greg Hamilton	Prudential Vista Real Estate, Anchorage, AK
Gay Hancock	Prudential Tropical Realty, New Port Richey, FL
Karla Hollett	Prudential DeHOFF REALTORS®, North Canton, OH
Bernadette Houston	Prudential New Jersey Realty, Westfield, NJ
Steve Janett	Prudential Janett Real Estate, Verona, NJ
Steven Johnson	Prudential Greater Topeka REALTORS®,Topeka, KS
William Kelly	Prudential Notas Real Estate, Somers, NY
Sally Kelman	Prudential Connecticut Realty, Stamford, CT
Sandy Kostedt-Townsend	Prudential Preferred Properties, Albuquerque, NM
Bob Lamberg	Prudential California Realty, Truckee, CA
Judith Law	Prudential Network Realty, Ponte Vedra Beach, FL
Beth Leegant	Prudential Connecticut Realty, Wilton, CT
Tina Leonard	Prudential Terry Horrocks Real Estate, Lake Placid, NY
Randi Lipkin	Prudential New Jersey Realty, Caldwell, NJ
Kim Litton	Prudential Volunteer Realty, Knoxville, TN
Eva Loken	Prudential Vista Real Estate, Eagle River, AK
Carlton Lund	Prudential California Realty, Carlsbad, CA
Lilah Field Lynn	Prudential Decker Realty, Virginia Beach, VA
Elizabeth Ann Macchio	Prudential Notas Real Estate, Somers, NY
Bob Majorino	Prudential California Realty, Thousand Oaks, CA
Charlene Mandeville	Prudential Mandeville Real Estate, Bozeman, MT
Denise Massey	Prudential Carson Properties, Carson City, NV
Lydia McCrary	Prudential Volunteer Realty, Knoxville, TN
Lory McGregor	Prudential California Realty, Encinitas, CA
David Melcher	Prudential California Realty, Yucaipa, CA
Steve Mickey	Prudential California Realty, Whittier, CA
John Nie	Prudential Locations, Alea, HI
Susan Nolte	Prudential Carruthers REALTORS®, Severna Park, MD
Jeanne Oughterson	Prudential Rochester Realty, Pittsford, NY
David Parrish	Prudential Highlands-Cashiers Real Estate, Highlands, NC
Michael Paull	Prudential Network Realty, Ponte Vedra Beach, FL
Nancy Pedicord	Prudential Florida Properties, Fort Lauderdale, FL
Page Pratt	Prudential Volunteer Realty, Knoxville, TN
Nanci Primley-Stenshoel	Prudential Northwest Properties, Battle Ground, WA
A. C. Robbins	Prudential Carolinas Realty, Chapel Hill, NC
Lois Rosenfield	Prudential Prime Properties Warwick, RI
Walter Schopfer	Prudential Floberg REALTORS®, Billings, MT
Rick Schulz	Prudential Bob Hatton Realty, Tampa, FL
Kathy Schulz	Prudential Bob Hatton Realty, Tampa, FL
Marcia Schwartz	Prudential California Realty, El Cerrito, CA
Nathaniel Scoble	Prudential Achievers Realty, Pickering, Ontario
Melissa Smoak	Prudential Network Realty, Jacksonville, FL
Henry Soucy	Prudential Rush Realty, Alton, NH
Marjorie Tomlinson	Prudential River Realty, Fredericton, NB
Tammy Trujillo	Prudential California Realty, Pleasanton, CA
Pamela Woolum	Prudential Residenz REALTORS®, Beavercreek, OH
Debra Wymore	Prudential Texas Properties, The Woodlands, TX
Elizabeth Zygowicz	Prudential Connecticut Realty, Farmington, CT

RockTalk Winter 98/99 21

Lois' community service award from Prudential, featured in Rock Talk magazine.

only top woman to win. I was honored at a spring luncheon at the hospital. I won $5000.00 and donated it all to the Frequent Flyer Fund at Hasbro Children's Hospital.

Leaving my Real Estate career to help Elaine with her babies and David due to his health I had much to do. When I made a donation to the Hole in the Wall Camp, a camp started by actor Paul Newman in 1988 for seriously ill kids in Ashford, Connecticut, I stopped in their offices in New Haven, Connecticut, left a donation and expressed interest in the camp's operation and asked for a visit to be able to see the camp in action as I was a retired registered nurse and soon that visit was made for me with the Director of Operations in a golf cart. I was so impressed that after I sent a thank you letter and I told them if they need help I was available and for the next 5 and a half years I did the Rhode Island Fundraising in Providence at the Federal Post Office and at the Navy base in Newport, Rhode Island. So much enjoyment to do this for the 'kids' and I was able to speak at these gatherings and I gave my all as best as I could.

Years fly by and during the time when the grand-kids were small I started to write children's stories and wrote a collection of seven stories as they grew. I had them typed up and put them in a closet for many years until a gal came to volunteer with David. She was a creative writing teacher at a college in Rhode Island and when I had her read the stories she immediately said they had to be published into a book. We contacted a self-publisher in Rhode Island and an appointment was made for me at the end of June 2018 and by October of 2018 my book was out and sales began. How proud I was. I started a separate business account and my book was sold on Amazon and I did a few book signings at Barnes and Noble and at my publisher's bookstore in Pawtucket. So much fun to sign the book for all who bought them - an achievement at then 83 years old.

Now I just finished another book: an adult one and I am waiting for editing and then to publish. Writing this Legacy book now becomes a full time job as it goes along...

I have started to write out my best recipes and stories, and to bring together favorite photos of my life - so many to choose from ...

As I look back on a life full to capacity I try to remember all the 'goodies' and try to forgo all the 'baddies'...

My best words will now come along to each and every one I love and have admired in this glorious time called Lois' moments ... a long time has evolved since I was born and my first cry of life on that cool October moment during the night of October 22, 1935. They did not know just what they all were in for with moi!!

How do you sum up a Lifetime Achievement reward for yourself without being too prolific in it all - why not, as every life is important no matter who you may be?

I gather at this now as I am approaching my 85th birthday - October 22, 2020. I suddenly feel that year I am there whether I want to be or not. You reflect on life lived and want to remember only all the good things out there but there is a limb you run into that prevents you - those troubles and stresses remain vividly in your memory - so how do you surpass this obvious tumult - remembering them. A good question and one hard to answer as these memories are what we lived through and tore at us at the times lived and remain heavy as part of our being.

Have you ever heard someone complain of their tsuris (troubles) (bad times) and suddenly you are playing I can top this! We all do that and that is in fact what releases us and does not help the other.

This is constant and somehow I believe this is a keep going tactic or just being a total pain to others - we all live our own ways to combat the bad times and somehow as we live we finally learn how and be able to handle it all - time heals it all and then you can handle whoever with the pounce you never thought you had in you -

My worst was when I had just finished a most wonderful party that I worked hard to prepare for and helped pay for – a delightful and beautiful day and evening event and as the people were leaving and saying goodbye all said what a wonderful time it was except one person - who it was I will not divulge but she was ready as I believe she was too jealous of us all and saw the right moment: "you are in for a big let down after this party- be careful!" Don't ever do that to anyone no matter who they may be. I survived my traitor lady and surpassed it all and am today who I am.

I love my children, my grandchildren, my entire family, my many friends - so endearing and the man I married and who was by my side for 62 years, David and our favorite doggy friends. Bitsy and even way back Tookie and Frisky Jane.

Life will go on I believe and people will remember the little red-head with pigtails who was a Frisky Jane herself - a tomboy- a darer to do it all, a survivor not like on TV, a caring and loving gal who was born at my house on 37 Highland St in Franklin, and later, now at Orleans Court in Warwick, Rhode Island.

You know there is so much else I know I should have written but you have to keep those secrets to yourself as they are private times that you would never believe of me.

With love and 'chutspah' to me.

Lois Stutman Lois Rosenfield Mrs. David Rosenfield

Clint Eastwood and me!
Hog's Breath Inn, Carmel, California, April 1983.

Bizrai
Lithuania

Joseph married Yenta Lea Chait (Etta Leah) in 1897

Etta had

2 brothers:	Shleima Bina	b. 1880
	Aryeh Leib	b. 1889
1 sister:	Mere Tsipe	b. 1889

(not sure if two in 1889 were twins but no multiple births noted)

Bizrai, Lithuania

Joseph and Etta's first child was

1. Chaya Miri (Ida) b 1898
2. Gedalyah b. 1900
   d. 1902
3. Sarah (Sally) b. 1902
4. Rebecca (Rivka) b. 1904
   'Aunt Belle'

There is some detail noted that Joseph, alone, may have come to America after Sarah's birth. He returned to Bizrai and his next 2 children were born

5. Azne (Ann) b. 1905

6. Goldye b. 1899

We believe Joseph returned to America alone in 1905 and may have come to relatives already here probably in the Boston / Roxbury area. Etta and the five girls apparently traveled to America in 1908 and believe the port of entry was Ellis Island.

Homesteads were first in West Medway, Massachusetts about 1908 and were farms with acreage....many acres by 1924. Mulkie (Sam) and Honey (Albert) were born In Medway, Massachusetts as there are birth records recorded in Medway Town Hall.

Joseph did many aspects of farming. He raised and sold cows and horses, butchered them, sold Kosher and non-Kosher cow meat and sold horse meat to kennels for dogs etc. to eat. They had a dairy business as well and Joseph killed sick horses for other farmers and had a special place built to do this his slaughter house so to speak. I remember going to the above with others to observe this. We know there was a fire at the old farm in West Medway and that the home was never rebuilt but the large area of farm, barns and pig pens were kept and toiled at when they moved to Holliston Farm on Washington St. in or around 1924-1925 or perhaps earlier.

Ida, the first child, married Maurice Stutman in 1921 and I do not think she ever lived at the Holliston Farm as Edie remembers Honey and Mulkie coming to visit at times and playing and helping to care for her after school.

Running the farms with many hired hands, was Joseph in charge. Ida and Belle helped as well but do not know about the others.

Ida and Goldye were the first to marry. Goldye married Israel Jack Freedman About 1925. Bobie Etta ruled the roost and was in charge of the money and the many ways to get it. She was her own banker and brainiac as was Aunt Belle. The $100 dollar bills were kept between the mattresses on the fluffy beds. It is not known of Sam's part in working the farm as he was the first to go to college at Northeastern (about 1930-1933) and received a Civil Engineering degree. Ann had graduated from Framingham Teacher's College and Sarah had taken Secretarial Courses and worked in that field. Belle, for the most part, ran everything later and had the mink and silver fox farm to run in the 1940's. These furs were all the vogue and they made lots of money doing this adding to the $100 dollar bills to hide. Feeding the foxes and catching them to put back in their pens, was exciting doings back then.

It is not known when the Ashland farm was bought but Aunt Edie had her 16th Birthday party there in the upper barn around 1938. The farm foreman, Frank and his family were caretakers and lived on the farm, not the Katseffs. It was then a big dairy business and Lois visited there many times. She started at the entrance of the barn and all the cows who were laying down received a 'kick' from her so they would get up. Indeed, all the cows knew when Lois arrived!

The Ashland farm area is now a Shaw's Market complex with many stores and businesses. It has passed into the future so they say.

Uncle Honey had the first of the first 'milk' stores there when he started his stores which became known as 'Honey Farms'.

Ida and Maurice Stutman first lived in Medway, Massachusetts where Edie lived during her early toddler years. Then they moved to the house on Highland St. in Franklin Massachusetts. Robert b. 1929, and Lois b. 1935, were raised there as well.

Maurice was a Master Electrician by trade. Edie went on to Framingham Teachers College for 1 1/2 yrs. and then married Sherwood Sadwin of Woonsocket, Rhode Island in 1942. They had two children: Lawrence b. 1943, and Darlene b. 1946. Edie has four grandchildren and four great-grandchildren. She married Dr. Saul Wittes in 1965.

Robert married Janet Simbol in 1952 and had four children: Marjorie b. 1953, Steven b. 1956, Alyson b. 1961, and Jennifer b. 1966. Robert worked at the farm for some years. He has six grandchildren and lives on Cape Cod with Evelyne. Robert was an electrician like Maurice and later worked for Sherwood (Edie's husband) in the curtain business.

Lois married David Rosenfield in 1956 and it was David's Uncle Ben who had married Aunt Ann Katseff way back, so at this wedding the families met and rejoiced once again. Lois and David have two children: Michael b. 1957, and Elaine b.1961. Michael is married to Beth and Elaine is married to Jonathan Gillim. Lois and David have four grandchildren and reside in Warwick, Rhode Island where this first Katseff Family Reunion is being held on August 14, 2010.

Goldye married Issac (Jack) Freedmen about 1925. They lived in Stonington ME. where they had three children: Rhoda b.1928, Harvey b. 1933, and Shirley b. 1936. Jack and his brothers owned a general store in Stonington for many years. Goldye died in 1986. Shirley lived with Aunt Sally, Uncle Phil and Richard in Brookline, MA during her High School years. Rhoda had married Jimmy Grace and had two children: Nadine b. 1949, and Stephen b. 1951. Rhoda re-married and had two more children: Emil b. 1958, and Joey b. 1965. Rhoda died in 1989. She leaves three grandchildren, two step-grandchildren and seven great-grandchildren. Harvey married Judith Harnch in 1959 and had two children: Forrest b. 1961, and Kirk b. 1964. Harvey has two grandchildren. Shirley married Donald Duffy on September 11, 1960 and has two children: Cheryl b. 1962, and Donald b. 1965. She has three grandchildren and will be married for 50 yrs. on Sept. 11, this year. Sally married Philip Holmes and had one child, Richard b.1943. She has two grandchildren and two great grandchildren. Sally died in 1993. She loved the beach and spent many summers in Onset, Massachusetts and Lynn, Massachusetts. The family was always invited especially Lois.

Rebecca (Belle) was the last of the Katseff girls to marry. She married Julius (Jay) Sandler in 1946 but had no children. She gave and did much for the family when the need arose and for many years she and Jay donated monies to Children's Hospital in Boston. Today a Tribute plaque hangs in the Parent and Doctor's meeting Room in the Cardiac Wing. This was done after their deaths in 2007.

Ann met Benjamin Russian and married in 1934. They had two children: Gerald b. 1936, and Susan b. 1938. Ann has four grandchildren and four great-grandchildren.

Ann died in 1996. She had been a school teacher and moved with Ben to Connecticut., Long Island, New York, and Woonsocket Rhode Island with Ben who was a draftsman.

Sam worked as a Civil Engineer after attending Northeastern University. He entered WW II and became an Ensign in the SeaBees (Navy) and his tour of duty was the clean-up in Hawaii following the bombing of Pearl Harbor, hit Dec. 7, 1941.

(He bought Lois her first grass skirt and was gracious to his nieces and nephews) Sam married Gertrude Chelemsky at the Beacon House in Brookline in 1952 and had two children: Howard b. 1952, and Peter b. 1956, and now have five grandchildren.

Sam died in 1980 and Gert in 1999. Sam had started London Records in the early 50's in Philadelphia. His hit recording was by Theresa Brewer called 'Music, Music, Music' and his other contract was with one Buddy Greco. Sam also owned a vacuum cleaner business after the war and later, a John Deere tractor Agency in Acton, Massachusetts.

Albert (Uncle Honey) worked and cared for the farms mostly the Whitney farm in Ashland, Massachusetts. He met and married Miriam Rosenberg in 1946 and had four children: Linda b. 1947, Robert b. 1950, Ellen b. 1955. and James b. 1962. Uncle Honey was the one who started Honey Farms by selling milk. He died in 1972. He has four grandchildren, one step-grandchild and three great grandchildren. Before marriages, Mulkie and Honey shared many good times with their buddies Joe and Sy Novick, Sam Ketover and Elliot and Paul Wexler.

Bobie and Zadie Katseff opened their home to many people and not just to family. There was always lots of food stocked and waiting to feed and entertain family and friends. They hosted family gatherings especially at Passover and other Holidays. They often entertained and their house was open to all. Bobie worked two kitchens to keep up with the many people. It was always good memories especially for the first of their grandchildren. We all had our fun times together and were devilish as most children are especially when we traveled up to the attic to peek at all the treasures stored up there! We would also crawl under the dining room table while the 'feast' was going on and giggle and laugh.

Life was simpler then. We were close and whenever one in the family needed something or were 'down on their luck' or were ill, they got help. That's what family did!

The memories are all still there. Later on, Edie hosted family Thanksgiving dinner in Woonsocket where she lived with her family. For all who are here today....WELCOME! And do keep the memories alive for future generations to come. We are family and the beat goes on.

Joe and Etta would bicker together in later life and Etta, in Yiddish, would say,

"Yosel, 1oz mere gumuph" 'LEAVE ME ALONE!

We should all be so glad she did not use that tactic in their earlier life!

We never would have been here today....ALL OF US!

Katseff Timeline

KATSEFF FAMILY TIMELINE (ONLY INCLUDING UP TO FIRST COUSINS (see Family Tree for subsequent data)

1875	Joseph Katseff born in Lithuania (one sister and three brothers)
1879	Etta Leah Chait is Born in Lithuania(who has one sister and two brothers (all moved to South Africa?)
12/1897	Joseph Katseff marries Etta Leah Chait
9/18/1898	Ida Katseff is born in Lithuania
9/15/1899	Goldye Katseff is born in Lithuania
10/26/1900	Getalya Katseff is born in Lithuania (dies on 8/29/1902 of a high fever)
6/29/1902	Sally (Sarah) Katseff is born in Lithuinia
2/15/1905	Belle (Rebecca) Katseff is born in Lithuinia
4/7/1905	Ann Katseff is born in Lithuinia
1905	Joseph Katseff returns to America (Boston/Roxbury area to visit/stay with existing relatives) for the second time (both times alone)
1908	Joseph makes arrangements for his wife and five daughters to come to America
1908	First Katseff homestead somewhere in or near Medway, MA
8/11/1911	Samuel Katseff is born on a farm in Medway, MA
9/10/1913	Honey (Albert) Katseff is born on a farm in Medway, MA
6/28/1921	Ida Katseff marries Maurice Stutman and moves off the family farm, but first remained in Medway, MA
1922	Edie Stutman is born
1924	The remaining Katseff Family moves to a farm in Holliston, MA
1925	Goldye Katseff marries Jack Freedman and moves off the farm (Jack's family own a General Store in Stonington, ME (Goldye and Jack moved to ME later in life).
1/14/1928	Rhoda Freedman is born
11/7/1929	Bobby Stutman is born in Franklin, MA (becomes a Master Electrician)
1929	Samuel Katseff goes to Northeastern University (small offices upstairs on Huntington Ave) to earn a degree in Civil Engineering

1933	Ann Katseff graduates from Framingham teacher's College
12/9/1933	Harvey Freedman is born
1934	Ann Katseff marries Ben Russian
10/22/1935	Lois Stutman is bom in Franklin, MA (becomes a nurse)
5/25/1936	Shirley Freedman is born
6/26/1936	Gerald Russian is born
1938	Edie Stutman has a 16th Birthday Party at the farm in Ashland, MA
8/21/1938	Susan Russian is born.
1942	Samuel Katseff joins the Navy and due to his Civil engineering degree is assigned to the Sea Bees as an initial rank of Ensign, by the end of WW II, Sam is now a Lieutenant (second class) but still does not know how to swim.
2/8/1942	Edie Stutman marries Sherwood Sadwin
1942	Sally Katseff marries Philip Holmes
6/26/1943	Lawrence Sadwin is born (technically a second cousin but this birth fits nicely into the timeline)
9/8/1943	Richard Holmes is born
1944	Ann Katseff and Ben Russian move to New York City
2/17/1946	Honey Katseff marries Miriam Rosenberg
8/24/1946	Darlene Sadwin is born (technically a second cousin but this birth fits nicely into the timeline)
12/1946	Belle Katseff marries Jay (Julius) Sandler
1/7/1947	Linda Katseff is born
3/12/1950	Robert Katseff is born
1/20/1952	Samuel Katseff marries Gertrude Chelemsky in Brookline MA (see Howard Katseff for the 16mm movie of the wedding (no sound)
6/1/1952	Robert Stutman marries Janet Simbol
11/24/1952	Howard Katseff is born
8/3/1955	Ellen Katseff is born
10/26/1956	Lois marries David Rosenfield (David's uncle is Ben Russian (married to Ann Katseffin 1934, one year before Lois is born)
11/5/1956	Peter Katseff is born
12/16/1962	Jimmy (James) Katseffis born

Descendancy

My maternal grandfather, Joseph Akivah Katseff: descendant from Ravel Mordechai Katseff (1849-?), and wife, Rachel – descendant from Gednlya Katseff (1829-1898).

They had five children:

1. Asna Malta Katseff
2. Yankel Aron Katseff (B. 1868)
3. Akivah Joseph Katseff (b.1875-19681)

   married Etta Leah Chait – maternal grandmother
4. Yitrzchax Katseff (b. 1862)
5. Mordachai Katseff (b. 1886)

Joseph and Etta had 8 children – One died at 2 years of age – Gedalyh (1900-1902)

1. Ida (1898-1958)

   married Maurice Stutman and had three children:

   1. Edythe (b. 1922)
   2. Robert (b. 1929)
   3. Lois (b. 1935)
2. Sarah (1902-1932)
3. Rebecca (1904-1997)
4. Ann (1905-1996)
5. Goldye (1908-1986
6. Samuel (1911-1980)
7. Albert (1913-1972)

My maternal grandmother: Etta Leah Chait Katseff: descendant from grandfather Izrael Chait to father Hanoch Hirsh Chait who was born in Bizrai, Lithuania and wife Chana Ita (1857-1940) in Lithuania.

They had four children

1. Etta Leah Chait (1879-1953)
2. Shleima Bina Chait (1880-1960)
3. Mere Tsipe Chait (1889-died in the Holocaust)
4. Aryeh Leib Chait (1889-1947)

Hanoch Chait had two siblings.

1. Shalom Leib (b.1860)
2. Shetzl Chait (b.1863)

My father: Maurice Stutman (1893-1952)

Ancestors of father:

Louis Stutman (1873?-1943), married Elizabeth (1873?-1934)

They had three children:

1. Maurice Stutman (1893-1952)
2. Hyman Stutman (June 7, 1900-?)
3. Rebecca Stutman (May 6, 1904-1957)

There is no other lineage.

My Nursing Career

I had and did many duties in my nursing career!

I did post-surgical staff at Kent County Hospital and worked in their post- partum maternity section for many years.

I went on to the Private Medical agencies and did staff and private duty at all the major hospitals in Rhode Island and then private duty in people's homes.

I could write a story about all the above but will just relay a couple stories to you.

One day shift I was doing at Rhode Island Hospital for the Medical Personnel Pool and there was a young 16-year old patient who came in with a seizure that occurred when she was working on a fishing boat - she had to be taken to Miriam Hospital for a special test and I was chosen to transport her in the ambulance to Miriam - before we left I made sure to have a taped throat stick with me just in case of a seizure - the nurse at Rhode Island said I would not need it as she was seizure-free since coming into Rhode Island Hospital.

The drive to Miriam went uneventful and as the ambulance backed into the Miriam Hospital ER parking area, my patient went into a Grand Mal seizure and I immediately inserted the taped throat stick into her mouth to prevent her from hurting herself severely.

After the seizure subsided the ambulance techs and I got her quickly into the Miriam ER and transferred her to staff doctors there. My job was done - I had saved her life.

And this story:

I had to transfer a private duty patient from his home in Barrington, RI to Rhode Island Hospital. He was very wealthy and had a limo and a Jamaican driver. We took the patient to the hospital and he was admitted. What is this nurse to do now - go back to Barrington in the limo by herself or wait at Rhode Island Hospital for my husband to pick me up as he had driven me to work that morning - *A* dilemma!

I be the "goodie" and waited for David at Rhode Island Hospital while the most handsome Jamaican driver took the limo back to Barrington.

My Travels

Many weekends and mid-weeks with David to B&Bs and to Stage Neck Inn and to our week in March at Edgewater Beach Resort in Dennis Port and weekdays in summer at the Cape.

We traveled to Hawaii (Maui) for my 50th birthday and to Aruba for our 35th anniversary and to Canada for our 50th back to our wedding trip destination with our children and grandchildren. And to California twice while Mike was at Berkeley and to Austin, Texas twice while Mike and family were there for his work.

By myself I traveled to Florida and went on five Viking cruises to many countries. First with Barbara Bartel to Paris and Normandy on a Viking river cruise. Then next with Ellie from California on a Mediterranean Odyssey cruise to London, England and then to Barcelona, Spain, Monte Carlo, Cofu in Greece, Dubrovnik in Croatia and Tuscany, Venice, and Naples, Italy.

Then with Lil to Key West and to Mexico, then with Barbara Bartel and friends to Cuba. My last cruise to Portugal was cancelled because of COVID-19.

Saw many places and, of course the Eiffel Tower and the many fashion shoips in Paris. Fun times!

My Favorite Friends

Many friends through the years I have been fortunate to have had.

My dearest friend, Judy Contardo, became my friend in 1970 and remained as such until her passing in July of 2019. Judy was a great cookie baker and early on in the friendship I was over at her kitchen while she was baking holiday cookies. There was one special cookie I tasted and oohed and aahhed while eating it and asked her the name, Judy's reply was: these are my "Christmas Orgasms" and you just had one!!

Early in my life there was Joanne Morris who I played dolls with and of course Roberta Franklin who I walked to high school every day with.

The many more from High school and to this day, Fran Vozzella, Anne O'Neil, and Rosalie. We talk frequently.

My mah jongg group and special friend Melanie Racioppi, Jen Garrahan, and Hilda Cameron and my niece Darlene, and always Phyllis Swartz and Judy Contardo .

My dear friend Irma Katz from Beth Israel - passing in 2007 too early.

Many more even my 100 year old neighbor Helen Abrams. You need friends in a lifetime that is what makes up a lifetime.

I will not go into my boyfriends as there were too many, but the one who became my favorite became my husband on October 21, 1956. I fell in love so quickly that all the rest were soon sent goodbye letters and were forgotten. I did have one first love as we all do - no name to be mentioned.

9/11/2001

As I sit at my desk on what was to be a beautiful, breezy sunny day in September I instead am looking sadly at our flag now at half-staff. Moving freely on this day – not in full glory as should be…

A little before 9 a.m. this morning when the day and, as such a back to work and Travel Tuesday was just getting underway – the first report came across the television screen- "A fire of suspicious origin at the tower of the World Trade Center in New York City" and then the aftermath of outrageous and devastating occurrences.

I was a little girl when Pearl Harbor was bombed. I still remember something of that time – the horror and tragedy of then but being so young not to relate to the full understanding of it all – more as you grow and hear and see and witness and realize and feel the deep impact of what is happening – you are there – fully -completely – as the events of today.

Maybe it was easier then not to have to really understand but will the child of today's world be the same – no – how can they be – are they allowed?

My first thoughts when the events began today – I must know the safety of my family – I was able to verify that fairly quickly with incoming and outgoing calls – my deep thankfulness for that – but what about the thousands of others – what will they do….

I spent most of the morning with my husband David glued to the TV – until I couldn't continue to watch - the chaos, horror, devastation, a freedom taken and destroyed and mutilated. So much no more and there was no warning if any – it was just made to happen – and horribly allowed. I am so angry, so hurt, so sad and just wished somehow to make this just into a dream – to wake up and everyone will all be fine - that I know couldn't be.

We will hear more details of actual facts for a very long time – but can we forget the first actuality of what happened on this September day in 2001 – planes full of live people, hijacked and then targeted and slamming and crashing into important buildings like the World Trade Center, the Pentagon filled with working people – happy and alive and then no more. My heart goes out to them, their families and to the many who helped to save and care for whoever survived, and maybe in helping gave their own lives.

This has not been a normal day – but we should go on – we have to – that must be!

Hello,
I'm Back

Hello, Mrs. Robin, how are you today and are you busy getting your nest ready for your new baby birds to be? It certainly is a glorious day, isn't it? And do you know what Mrs. Robin?, I'm going for a nice walk today and guess what – I saw the sun shining brightly when I awoke today. You know it's been so long since I saw the sunshine – oh yes, it's been there, but my life has been so troubled with all of life's problems and turmoil that for a very long time there were just heavy clouds above me and the days went by and I disappeared from myself. I didn't even hear you singing, Mrs. Robin, until today.

I just rushed from my bed and eagerly awaited the aroma and taste of my morning coffee- how delicious it was. Gosh, I had to make a list of things to do – summer is before us – I can't remember how long it's been since everything became a chore and desire was lost into a struggle to exist. I guess I just needed to hear you sing Mrs. Robin and I'm glad you're back. I think I am too….

I allowed my life to become what it was. I pushed and pushed and did and took and then it all turned into anger and it locked tightly inside of me. It became too much, too overwhelming, and then all my doing didn't mean anything. I was taken and I didn't even know.

I guess what occurs is that life goes along and seems to prevail. We do what we do and have to do and can do and then something happens. Something triggers the turn. Maybe an illness, a death of a family member or a friend, a fear, even a joy. Something then, either the immediate let down, or as I, the push. The push to do so much. The taking and then the defense build-up and the anger and then the swallowing of the anger and the result – hey -I'm not me, am I?

It's funny, at least I can admit to humor, now that one can creep into a state of being such as this. And then, one fine day, suddenly wake up and say, "What the hell. I'm Alive, I'm me!' I can't do everything or change things. Life is here to live, not to be tortured in turmoil. To be realized and appreciated and to be taken n the best and most healthy way possible – such as a young child, as he takes his first few steps – one step at a time with gumption and a will to continue and thus we must take that next step too – without the fear of tomorrow.

Realization, acceptance, necessity, willing and doing; only now with relaxation and knowing just how much you can do and will do not for others so much, but for you, alone, as the important one. We change, it can change, it will change. Do it for you, wake up and allow it to be and it will!

Good bye Mrs. Robin, I'm off for my walk. See you tomorrow. Did you know it's going to be another sunny day?!

My Thoughts on the Upcoming Election

My thoughts on a very warm day in February 2020 - will reach close to 60 degrees today and I am trying to get better from a head cold and cough and will soon open up my deck door and breathe in the warm air.

We will soon choose a Democratic candidate for the Presidential election November 3, 2020 who will face Donald Trump - the President of the United States for the last four years - a most disliked President. This election will be a very interesting one to say the least.

We have had so much happening of late and now many shootings and fires and such that although so bad has become a common occurrence - sad and many people hurt or killed and fires in California and other areas and Australia just recently.

I feel so bad about it all and as others cannot help or control this from happening - very sad to hear and to witness ...then the latest in climate change and the frequency of hurricanes and tornadoes with all the loss and destruction makes this aged Senior very upset and at a loss to help the situation.

As of the end of January 2020 a new virus has begun called the Coronavirus - starting in China and fastly moving into other European countries and now cases in the United States. It is a very scary situation and people are greatly using caution to protect themselves and their loved ones from it all. I can only pray for all and hope for the best and find a vaccine to stop this and release us from what is happening world-wide. I am a praying person so I say: Please God, help us through this!

We keep updated on the news of it all on TV- CNN, etc but now the news is no fun to hear.

I hope that we can have a more peaceful time future -wise and by no way can we go back to the times of my birth as that was hard Depression times. But to a more peaceful and comfortable time to live in for what may be a time ahead for my dear ones I love and to mankind and Womankind in general.

Corona Virus
Covid - 19

It all started in January of 2020 - slowly word of a virus was passing through the news. My concern at the time was for my grandson's trip at the end of 2019 to areas near and to India and to be home on January 21 on a Tuesday in 2020.

Little did I know until the later that the first case of COVID-19 in the US was in Seattle, Washington; a man who had traveled to Wuhan in China and had returned and then experiencing symptoms and had visited a nursing home in Seattle a place that thus was contaminated by him and many patients then got the virus and many deaths. The Start; January 21, 2020.

Wuhan, China then became the epicenter of the virus with many cases and deaths - then Italy and Spain and other countries became epicenters and the US took over starting in Washington State and then quickly infested the entire country with NY in New Rochelle, NY where a lawyer having traveled overseas came back and then his city became heavily involved and then NYC and other states with much damage and deaths to follow. My own state of Rhode Island - at the present day of April 16, 2020 - now becoming the 'Hot Spot" with many cases and deaths. Our Governor Gina Raimondo giving us updates every day and the National Guard brought in and beaches and parks closed as well as malls, stores, restaurants, salons, businesses here and everywhere.

Never ever have we experienced this as bad before the flu and loss of lives in 1918 and Pearl Harbor and 9/11 was bad enough and other types of viruses but not as dangerous and fast moving and cases as many as this in just weeks. So many getting the virus and dying so quickly We were vitally caught without enough masks, gowns, ventilators, health workers and how to counteract with medications. We were at a loss and research showed no intermediate treatments - what to use and treat and is there a way to somehow find a needed vaccine.

Stay at home, wear masks, socially distance to 6 feet, no visits to relatives in hospitals or nursing homes or assisted living, senior hours at grocery markets to shop, not safe to go to CVS or post office or Target. Luckily to have a younger person to shop at grocery store for you or they too are in danger: fear, anxiety, high blood pressure. Sadly losing loved ones and not able to be there for them to hold their hand and to say "goodbye" - so very sad. Waiting and suddenly finding out that you know someone who has come down with it and still other illnesses happening non-related to the virus.

Staying in, cleaning where you never had found time to do before. Baking and eating too much, being alone in your home and only be able to face time and zoom to see your loved ones - holding in your feelings and phoning and texting and emailing your friends and family. Apprehension, sadness for all, and the TV news being constant and mind boggling to say the least - but still humor prevails with jokes and we can still laugh. Whatnext?

There has been now weeks that have gone by and where are we? Theentire US infested more in certain areas than others but insanely heavy with cases and loss of lives - terribly high losses of young and old - many in nursing homes. So very traumatic and grossly sad!

So many stories and many so sad that how can you not get depressed! But strength has to maintain itself to prevail.

So many people out of work as un-employed now. So many confined to home to work. So many families separated and not being able to be together and only by face time or zoom if you be fortunate to be able to do that - still heart-wrenching. Health care workers exhausted and unable to see their own loved ones; people in quarantine in their own homes and so many infected with the disease at home or having to be in hospitals sick and many on ventilators.

We were caught hands down unable to survive if you be one with immune system that is not able to handle the plague of deception.

It controls the TV constantly and so much input by people, doctors, journalists, health workers STILL trying to estimate exact causes and what best to do in situation of unknown knowledge to find the cause - try this medication, try that, no vaccine yet to be developed - maybe this, maybe that, still not sure about trying meds used for other conditions to some may help not others - horrible times as of this writing on April 17, 2020.

Our President Donald Trump is now in charge of the situation here - he be the lucky one to have to handle this with his own Task Force of notable people who have medical backgrounds plus others who have not and trying to keep us informed each day of what is happening so far - enlightening us with compassion as they see fit - a job that is not an easy one but yet here they are and we have to believe that what they say is what it really is! How can you as the President put across all this with no highlight of compassion in his voice - just reading from a prepared list each day so people can hear the update briefing . We need compassion - we do all of us.

Now after the time that has elapsed so far, President Trump has set before us and to the Governors of each state his guideline phases to be able when we can re- open their states to recovery options as the Governors so decree to do as what they consider is correct time elements to do and to handle what is treated wisely and properly and protectively right to do.

Difficult as we DO NOT KNOW yet as we STILL embracing the negativity of it all and the fear and anxiety of what is right and what is wrong. Hell on wheels and rolling like mad is uncertainty - a highly scary and questionable situation but can we even yet think to do the above yet at this time?

Would we even imagine in our lifetime that this crazy war of the world be upon us and catch us in such an off guard time and infect a population of people so fast and furious and the world economy just shutting down and closed signs everywhere and children walking without adults with masks on and fearful of the times on hand - wearing gloves also for protection - the new present normal - how very strange to see all this - no school but at home as teachers try to keep classes going with virtual teaching - as parents try to work from home and keep little ones busy and distancing and each trying to carry on and survive - an exhausting situation to have achieved and no graduations in high school or college.

Facts and figures prevail and climbs higher and higher and yes, it will peak soon but still grows. Honestly, it is a chore to live with and handle - yikes the days go by and now we are closing in on May 1. What will we see then?

The thing that is so difficult to watch and see are the way the health care workers have to dress to protect themselves for hours at a time with masks and cover-ups and how this has to last for the period of time they work with most just short breaks and pressure from masks marking their faces ever showing bruises from long endurance but yet they are there holding hands and speaking softly and tenderly to patients and telling them they are there as the patient closes their eyes and breaths stop and they die alone - so alone but for the tenderness of the medical crew - their heroes.

I be a former, now retired Registered Nurse and I see now with what is actually going on but in ultra-strong performance of those on duty to cover the entire hospital slew of admissions for this virus - so frequent and so many that have to prevail by going on scary ventilators and many for long periods of time before they hopefully can recover with whatever meds are tried and those others who have no chance at all with maybe also underlying existing conditions where by their chances are strong for survival - a miracle... and those who do survive - an unexpected chance again for life.

How can I as one at my age of 84, now living alone in a condo and only able to see my immediate family by either text, email, face time or zoom - I say thank the good Lord for this updated technology but still it is not easy for anyone young or old.

Our normalcy is a new endeavor we are faced with and we carry on sadly but thankfully, we at least have as above so we carry one - day to day living is so the same and we hope that health and home problems stay good as managing these other problems are super trying and you can feel the anxiety and stress prevail when mentioned happenings occur. Humor relaxes you for a little bit but the incredible times prevail until we can see the light of a new day of the wave descending and not increasing. DO not want to hear the latest counts as it is mind-boggling to see the numbers come up on the TV screen each day. Horrendous losses of people - loved ones - our many seniors with less chance and to know that someone's small child has been lost - a trying occurrence - we all cry for those we did not even know.

Today is April 22, 2020 and as I read the tallies of cases in RI, Providence alone has 1,524 cases and Pawtucket 496. Cranston has 331, North Providence 314, East Providence 251 and my Warwick 195 with Central Falls 183 and Woonsocket 161. Other towns the lesser - an amazing tally- but yes it is thus.

I myself have been ok until realizing that my blood pressure rising to not normal heights and my doctor having to increase my already existing meds to double the amount to help bring the high amount down to again normal rates. Scary as it just happens to me as everybody in these difficult times – hopefully, nothing else unrelated to the virus happens to me or others. We just do not know...

My thoughts are written and this is the truth of just what has happened to the world at this present time. Unreal, surreal, and positively yes.

Can we know the future - only time will tell and that is still unknown... what will be in the Fall and next winter - will it come back and even more intense s it has now - hopefully not and maybe a vaccine researched and developed as a preventative to be had and able to be used for the people - just a Please God and Praise God if so be...

I am sad for all those consumed with this plague or infection and who have passed and to their families and friends - my heart goes out to all - praise and thank you to all the health care workers, first responders, police, EMTs, firemen, helpers, workers - all who now give their own time to help the entire situation in lieu of their own health and families to do their job to save the others. Heroes yes and outstanding men and women - more than heroes who prevail for us - these people need care .

When I Was Young, I Did This!

1. I skied and sledded across the street on the hills.
2. I skated at Snake Pond with all the other kids near my house.
3. I played Hide and Seek and Kick the Can with my neighbor's kids.
4. I planted a vegetable garden in my back yard.
5. I mowed the grass.
6. I cleaned the house when my mother told me to even vacuumed.
7. I walked to school - went to one room Brick School for 1st and 2nd grade.
8. I walked to schools for 3rd to 12th grade at a distance from my house - sometimes getting a ride from my mother or with friends.
9. I was Valedictorian in the 8th grade - spoke about nursing which became my career - first one.
10. Played sports in high school - field hockey, basketball and softball.
11. Was in OSKEY Show in high school even though I could not carry a tune - sang duet with Roberta.
12. Slid under porch to be a devil by myself- not afraid.
13. Saw TV for first time in early 50's.
14. Walked one mile to uptown by myself and back.
15. Kissed a boy in the Common after dance class.
16. Went parking with Ronnie at the Town Dump for two hours and then got a scolding at home as I came home late.
17. Had friends club in high school and we celebrated all our birthdays with parties.
18. Spent summer vacations with Aunt Sally in Onset and two weeks in Wellfleet with Edie and family during high school years - had fun.
19. Was a visitor at friend's home even when not invited - just walked in and said: 'Tm here."
20. Babysat at Sewell's - two houses down from mine and babysat with brother of fellow who later started CVS by name of Goldstein.

21. Got my driving license in high school after being in first driver ed course.

22. Went swimming with my friends at Lake Pearl and Lake Archer and at Town Swimming Hole as it was called and took swimming lessons there in the dark murky water.

23. Graduated high school 4th in my class - tough year as my daddy died the first week of my senior year.

24. Spent a lot of visits at my grandparents' farm.

25. Won only award at high school graduation - Francis Eddy King Scholarship of $300.00 -$100 from my class paid for ½ tuition to Beth Israel School of Nursing. Returned this award at my 50th Class Reunion in the amount then in 2003 of $1000.00.

26. Climbed trees with no fear.

27. Helped shovel snow.

28. Sat on open porch in summertime - no screens.

29. Had dogs – Cocoa, Snooky, and Marshmallow.

30. My brother Bob was always a devil and once at the farm put me on a pony with no saddle and made the pony go. He carried me piggyback down on grandparent's stairs and dropped me and I hit my head and blacked out. Doctor had to come - as you can see I am close to 85 years and still lucid. *I ALSO RAN INTO HIS ARMS THE DAY MY DADDY DIED AND HE HELD ME TIGHTLY UNTIL I STOPPED SHAKING.*

Bob was in a truck accident when he was working at the farm and almost died. He married Janet and had four children, Margie, Steven, Alyson, and Jennifer.

He and Janet divorced in early 80s after 30 years of marriage and he became partner with Eveline for nearly 30 years until his death in 2017.

He was an electrical contractor and worked at Sadwin Curtains for many years as Vice President. He lived for many years in his home at Cape Cod in Eastham.

My only brother was six years older than me and was a great tease...miss him.

Things I Get Upset and Angry About

(In no particular order)

1. Bullying.
2. Sexual abuse to women.
3. Domestic abuse of all kinds.
4. Racism.
5. Anti-Semitism.
6. The Holocaust.
7. Discrimination.
8. Boasting, especially to lesser people.
9. Sly looks.
10. Are you wearing your hearing aide?
11. True obesity.
12. Snobbery.
13. Trump.
14. Fears that should not be.
15. Not being recognized in a fancy store ala "Pretty Woman".
16. Kids being sick – it hurts to observe this.
17. Family squabbles and not talking to each other.
18. Giving something to someone else when a first person should have been the recipient.
19. Unkind comments toward others.
20. Using people to better oneself.
21. Godless people.
22. Alcoholics and druggies.
23. Why homelessness and panhandling are necessary.
24. The F--- word.

Bubbe Etta, and Mama Ida's How to Cook Page

1. A short cup of hot water.
2. A smidge of salt.
3. One cracked egg to a pound of hamburger.
4. A sprinkle of cinnamon.
5. A handful of nuts, raisins, or chocolate.
6. Hershey's syrup in hot milk for cocoa.
7. About a tablespoon of chicken fat in the chopped liver.
8. Crumble the dough over the cake.
9. Use cold water in pie dough.
10. Two handfuls of luchshen (egg noodles) for a kugel.
11. Chopped egg and celery for a quick salad.
12. Break up a few matzo's for fried matzoh.
13. Hot coffee for flavor in the honey cake.
14. Cut up onions and cry.
15. A little bit of honey in tea for a cold.
16. Shaved corn in the chowder.
17. Cabbage soup with sugar for taste and lemon juice.
18. Corn latkes for Thursday supper.
19. Use the gribenes from making chicken fat in chopped liver.
20. Gribenes made a good sandwich too.
21. Pierogies, knishes, strudel – use a bit of this and that.
22. Let the challah rise then bake.
23. Will the meringue stay high - do not jump.
24. Oatmeal for winter breakfast.
25. Chicken on Friday, fish on Thursday meatloaf another day and whatever the other days.
26. Taste it first – may need more salt.
27. Never eat miltz or ITAH-you'll gag.

Recipes

Blueberry Buckle Cake

Mix together ¾ c. sugar, ¼ c. margarine or butter, 1 egg

Stir in 1/2 c. milk

Sift and stir in 1 ½ c. flour, 2 tsp baking powder, ½ tsp salt

Add: 2 cups drained blueberries (optional – chocolate chips or other fruit instead)

375° for 45 minutes until tester is clean

Topping optional – cinnamon, nuts, brown sugar, and butter.

Sugar Pecan Holiday Crisp Cookies

¾ c. butter

2/3 c. sugar

1 egg

1 tsp vanilla

½ tsp salt

1 ¾ c. flour

½ c. finely chopped pecans

Cream together butter and sugar until light. Beat in egg, vanilla and salt. Gradually stir in flour. Shape dough into 2 rolls or logs. Roll both in pecans and wrap in plastic wrap. Chill thoroughly. slice and bake – minutes or until browned. 350° oven.

Holiday Honey Cake

To 1 c. boiling water, add:

1 tsp cinnamon

1 tsp nutmeg

1 tsp allspice

2 tsp unsweetened cocoa

1 tsp instant coffee

Set this mixture aside.

In electric mixer, mix 3 eggs with 1 ½ c. sugar.

Add: 1 c. honey and ¾ cup oil. Then add 3 c. all-purpose flour with 1 tsp baking soda.

Pour the water mixture (with the spices) into batter slowly. Mix thoroughly and then add ¼ c. golden raisins and ½ c. nuts if desired.

Decorate with slices of almonds.

350° for 1 hour in 10” tube pan.

Lemon Tea Bread

¼ c. butter softened

½ c. sugar

1 egg

½ tsp – 1 Tbsp lemon to taste

1 Tbsp grated lemon peel

¾ c. flour

dash of salt

½ tsp baking powder

¼ c. milk

Lemon Glaze

1 Tbsp lemon juice

2 Tbsp 10X confectionary sugar

Cream butter and sugar and add egg and lemon peel. Beat well, then add flour, baking powder and salt, add milk and mix well.

350˚ until tester clean.

325 ˚ is better so it won't burn the bottom and stick – Yummy.

One Bowl Apple Cake

2 c. diced apples

¾ c. sugar

1/3 c. oil or butter

1 egg beaten

1 ½ c. unsifted flour

1 tsp vanilla or almond extract

1 tsp baking soda

1 tsp baking powder

1 tsp. cinnamon

½ tsp salt (optional)

½ c. raisins

Combine diced apples and sugar and let stand for 10 minutes

Mix following with spoon using one bowl:

Mix oil or butter into apple mixture. Combine dry ingredients then mix well. Stir in raisins, (I like golden raisins) and vanilla.

Bake in an 8" square pan at 350° for 35-40 minutes. Cool and cut.

Nantucket Bike Path Cookies

Grease cookie sheet.

¾ c. unsalted butter

½ c. light brown sugar

½ c. white sugar

1 egg

1 tsp cognac or vanilla extract

1 c. plus 2 Tbsp flour

½ tsp baking soda

½ tsp seal salt or regular salt

¾ c. semi-sweet chocolate chips

Cream butter and sugars. Beat until light. add egg and cognac or vanilla extract. sift flour, baking soda and salt. Stir into mixture. Add chocolate chips. Bake at 350° for 10-15 minutes. Cookies bake light and lacy. Delish.

Best Gluten-free Chocolate Chip Cookies

½ c. butter unsalted

1 Tbsp milk or almond milk

¾ c. light brown sugar

¼ c. white sugar

1 egg

2 tsp vanilla

1 ½ c. gluten-free flour

1 tsp baking soda

½ tsp salt

1 c. chocolate chips

In medium bowl whisk together the flour, baking soda and salt until evenly combined and set aside.

Melt butter in a saucepan over medium heat. Once butter melts, start to whisk constantly.

First butter will begin to foam then after a couple minutes it will begin to brown on the bottom of the saucepan. Turn off heat then add butter. Will give off a nutty odor. Pour into glass mixing bowl to prevent burning.

Add milk, and brown and white sugar. Whisk to combine. Add egg and vanilla and whisk to combine. Add egg and vanilla and whisk until smooth and creamy. Mix in dry ingredients. Stir in chocolate chips.

Cover bowl and let sit for 30 minutes. Preheat oven to 350°. Scoop cookie dough into about 2 Tablespoons of dough and place a few inches apart on a cookie sheet. Bake 10-12 minutes until golden and center is soft. Let cool 5 minutes then transfer to rack. For dairy free us Earth Balance

Banana Bread

Grease loaf pan

Beat until mashed 3 soft bananas

Sift together in bowl 1 ¾ c. flour, 2 tsp baking powder, ¼ tsp salt, ¼ tsp baking soda, 2/3 c. sugar

Add 1/3 c. unsalted butter or margarine, 2 eggs beaten, 1 c. nuts (optional)

Golden raisins and blueberries are optional

Bake 350° for 1 hour or until tester is clean.

Nice and Spicy Bread Pudding

6 slices cinnamon raisin bread

2 eggs

¼ tsp salt

2 c. milk

1 Tbsp butter

1/3 c. sugar

1 tsp vanilla

cinnamon on top

Cut bread into cubes and place in a shallow buttered baking dish. Heat milk and butter until hot. Do not boil. Beat eggs, sugar and vanilla constantly. Pour over bread. Let stand 5 minutes. Sprinkle lightly with cinnamon. Bake 350° for 50 minutes or until custard sets. Bake in pan with hot water ½ the depth of the pan. Makes 6 servings.

Janet's Apple Crisp

Pare about 6-8 apples in a dish. Mix cinnamon and sugar. Put apples and cinnamon mix in 8" greased pie plate. Bake covered with foil for 15 minutes at 400°.

Then, cream 1 c. sugar, ½ c. butter or margarine. Add 2 eggs beaten.

Sift and add to above:

1 c. flour

1 tsp baking powder

add 1 tsp vanilla

Pour over apples and bake until top is brown and tester is clean.

Anti Pasto

Romaine

shredded lettuce

black olives

cheese chunks and strips

cheddar and mozzarella

Bermuda onion

ham strips

pepperoni pieces

kielbasa chunks

egg – hard cooked wedges

jar of hot red peppers

cherry or grape tomatoes

cut up artichoke

fresh mushroom slices

anchovies

diced hard cooked eggs over top

Boursin cheese cubes (optional)

Look to make beautiful

Grilled Shrimp Salad

Grilled shrimp

paprika

pepper

bacon pieces

Romaine

Cherry tomatoes

Corn kernels

Grated carrot

Avocado

Lemon juice

Olive oil

Dijon mustard to taste

New Red and Yellow Potatoes

Microwave potatoes then split

Combine chive and onion cream cheese spread. Add ½ c. milk. Mix until smooth. Pour over sliced potatoes. Sprinkle with dill.

Oven BBQ Chicken (Gloria)

2 frying chickens cut up

Flour with pepper and brown in oil. Put in baking pan.

Cut up 2 medium onions and 1- 4oz. package of mushrooms and fry in margarine.

Dice 1 green pepper, 2 stalks of celery, 1 ½ c. catsup, 2 c. water and mix ingredients and pour over chicken. Cover with foil and bake at 350° for 1 ½ hours or until tender. Serve with steamed rice or Near East rice.

Sweet Potato Salad

2 large sweet potatoes(baked)

combine 2 Tbsp light mayonnaise and 1 Tbsp Dijon mustard

Cut and chunk cooked sweet potato

Red pepper

Celery

Red onion

toast pecans or almonds. Put in pineapple tidbits. Add and mix in mayo and mustard mix. Also can add and mix in broccoli, peas, corn, zucchini.

Nectarine Brown Rice Salad

Boil 1-3.5oz bag brown rice

Put rice in bowl. Add chopped nectarines, 1/3 c. chopped almonds or pecans, 1 Tbsp vegetable oil, 1 ½ tsp balsamic vinegar. Combine and serve at room temperature.

Rice Noodle Pilaf

2 handfuls fine noodles

¾ stick of margarine

Lightly brown noodles in margarine. Add 1 c. minute rice to noodles.

In separate pan, 2 ¼ c. water and 5 chicken bouillon cubes. Cook until bouillon dissolves. Add to rice and noodles on low flame. Simmer 5 minutes. Good with brisket and chicken BBQ.

Roasted Brisket

1 4 ½ - 5 inch flat brisket

Season with garlic powder and pepper.

Slice 3 small onions over.

Combine in pan

1 12oz. can of ginger ale (diet or regular)

¾ c. catsup

¾ c. golden raisins

Cook until warm and pour over brisket. Cover with foil. 350° for 45 min. of an hour then 325° until tender – 2 hours. Enjoy as is, delish

Mother's Sweet and Sour Meatballs

3 lb. chuck hamburger

Mix hamburger with 2 eggs, pepper garlic powder, 4 slices chale (hard) -wet with water, grated onion

Sauce:

3 cut up onions

½ c. sugar

1 Tbsp lemon juice

1 can tomato sauce (no salt or regular)

Boil above in ½ c. water for about 15 min. Then pop in meatballs – cocktail size. Boil and watch ¾ hour. Pour in over dish to brown. Yummy.

Fish Marinade

Olive oil

Red pepper

White wine

Fresh minced garlic

Black pepper

Combine to broil or bake fish

Bitsy's Gizzard Stew

Take about 1-2 lbs. of gizzards including chicken livers and put some salt and pepper in a pan and cover with water and boil until gizzard meat is soft. Remove any bones and cool until lukewarm and serve your puppy or dog – they will lap it up as it is yummy.

Play Bitsy Ball

Go outside with your dog to the top of the side of your hill. Take a round soft ball and throw in the air. Your dog will jump and catch the ball with his or her nose and then roll the ball down the hill with said nose. So much fun as you have to catch the ball and bring it back up the hill and start the game again. Fun and exercise.

Blessings

Holiday Greetings

New York wedding, September 1997